Bath in

A guide to the city's building stones

Elizabeth Devon   John Parkins   David Workman
Bath Geological Society

A Brief History of the Buildings in Bath

Before you walk you may like to sit and read a little of the background to the story which will unfold as you walk. The walk begins on page 4.

The mists of time

Legend has it that Bladud, eldest son of King Ludhudibras (9th century BC) was infected with leprosy and had to leave the kingdom. He became a swineherd but unfortunately the pigs he was tending also caught leprosy. He noticed that after the pigs had bathed in the hot waters by the River Avon, their skin began to heal. He tried too and his leprosy disappeared. He is said to have built a palace above the hot swamp. Perhaps, if he did, he used the local stone; we shall never know.

Roman Baths

The image of present-day Bath was formed in the 18th century, but the site was first developed by the Romans shortly after they came to Britain in AD 43. All the Roman buildings used the local *Bath Stone*. The remains of the Roman baths show, by the sound, unweathered nature of the stone used, that it was mined. The site of this activity is not known but is thought to be on the south side of Bath near the Fosse Way.

Saxon Bath

The collapse of the Roman empire in about AD 410 left the native inhabitants of Britain to continue the Romanised way of life. The buildings of Bath were certainly maintained for a while probably until AD 577 when the Saxons took over the city. The existing buildings were allowed to decay and the Roman way of life was no longer followed. However, it was not a dark age for the use of *Bath Stone*. It was still required for monastic houses, defensive walls and so on, but the Saxons often took what they needed from former Roman buildings rather than undertaking new quarrying. This means that *Bath Stone* blocks, first dug and worked by the Romans, may have been re-used many times and may still be in use in buildings today. In the 8th century St Peter's Abbey was built in Bath, probably largely from reworked Roman Stone. No trace of this building survives.

Norman rebellion

Saxon Bath was ravaged in a rebellion by Norman bishops in 1088. Construction of a new, larger abbey (demolished in its turn 400 years later) began soon after. Although stone from both Roman and Saxon buildings would undoubtedly have been used, new stone would also have been required and this would probably have come from Box, a few miles east of the city. It is known that *Box Ground Stone*, a very fine quality oolitic building stone was used for many large buildings such as Malmesbury Abbey (7th century) and Longleat House (1580).

Narrow streets

For the period from the 12th century to the 15th century, records are rather scarce but by the 15th century the Norman *Abbey* was in ruins. Details of the present Abbey, begun in 1499, are given later in this guide.

In 1654, the diarist John Evelyn recorded, *"This toune is entirely built of stone, but the streets, narrow, uneven and unpleasant."* However, in 1688 Samuel Pepys visited Bath and recorded that he found the town - *"most of stone, and clean, though the streets generally narrow."* (He also admired the "very fine ladies" who shared the baths with him!)

A golden age

The golden age for the use of *Bath Stone* was in the 18th and 19th centuries. In 1710 Ralph Allen came to Bath. He began to develop the quarries of Combe Down and Hampton Down, only about 2.4 km (1½ miles) from the River Avon but with a drop of some 150m (500 feet). Allen solved the problem of moving blocks of stone weighing several tonnes by making a tramway (the present Ralph Allen Drive) and engaged the Bristol engineer, John Padmore, for its construction. Two horses were used to pull the loaded trucks on the level and to return the empty ones uphill but the loaded trucks descended the long hill by gravity with ingenious controls to brake or stop the trucks on the steepest part of the hill. The tramway was built in 1731 and the river made navigable to Bristol in 1727. Ralph Allen's partner was the architect, John Wood, a native of Bath. Together they set the scene for fashionable Georgian Bath, made possible by the availability locally of abundant supplies of good quality *Bath Stone.*

Stone by railway

As transport improved, first with the canals and then the railways, *Bath Stone* began to rival **Portland Stone** as a popular choice of freestone for public buildings in many cities. Railways, however, also made possible the introduction of new types of stone into Bath and these can be seen in the great variety of cladding materials used in the city from Victorian times to the present day.

Bomb damage

Before the Second World War, Bath was probably the most beautiful city in England but in 1942 it suffered bomb damage. A good deal of the original Georgian centre was rebuilt after the war partly in pastiche style, using Georgian features, and partly in modern styles. *Bath Stone* was often used.

Bath Stone returns

The Bath Act of 1925 ruled that new buildings must be faced with a substance resembling *Bath Stone.* Freestone had become too expensive to work so a substitute was developed, based on crushed limestone. However, in the present City Centre area, natural stone is specified exclusively for new construction.

The City Centre and Classical Bath

The City Centre walk starts in the Abbey Courtyard, outside the Tourist Information Office which is housed in Abbey Chambers on the south side of Bath Abbey (the main walk is shown in yellow on the map inside the rear cover).

Abbey Chambers

The building of Abbey Chambers which houses the Tourist Information Centre is made of **Bath Stone**. (The age of any stone printed in bold oblique can be found in the table on page 46. A glossary of rock names is on pages 43-44). *Bath Stone* can be seen in the buildings all around this courtyard.

The stone here has been sawn into 'ashlar' blocks. These are rectangular blocks of stone, with faces precisely sawn. The unseen back face only might be left roughly hewn. Ashlar work is laid in even courses using a very fine mortar bed not normally exceeding 3mm wide. When the mortar is set, a wall may be tooled over to give as fine a surface as possible. Because of the amount of skilled labour required, ashlar work was (and still is) expensive. It tends therefore to be used mainly on front elevations. In most Georgian houses in Bath there is a striking contrast between the smooth and even ashlar front elevations and the irregular surfaces of the side and rear walls.

Now walk across the courtyard to look closely at the wall on the south side of the Abbey. (You will have to ignore the people who think you are rather odd staring at the wall.)

The blocks of *Bath Stone* here are very coarse, especially near the middle of the wall where you can see the remains of fossils. These are shells, mostly of bivalves, oyster-like creatures that lived in the sea in which the

rock formed. You can also see tiny, spherical ooids (page 5) which make up the rock. Can you see small wavy lines? These indicate movement of the particles by the currents in the sea. Look for these wavy lines in other places on the walk.

The formation of Bath Stone

Much of Bath is built of *Bath Stone*, a beautiful cream-coloured limestone, quarried and mined in the hills to the south and east of the City. *Bath Stone* is a general term, covering a group of stones quarried within an area about 10 km across from the west of Bath on one side to Corsham on the other. The quality of the stone varies a great deal according to the bed being worked and the location of the quarry. *Bath Stone* comes from the Jurassic Great Oolite Limestone. It is one of the very distinctive English building stones. We know it has been worked in Bath for nearly 2000 years since there are Roman buildings constructed of it.

A warm shallow sea

When *Bath Stone* was formed, some 170 million years ago, the area that is now the British Isles and Europe was between latitudes $30°N$ and $40°N$ and this region was covered in a warm, shallow sea. In places the sea floor was covered in spherical grains of calcium carbonate which, in the rock, resemble fish roe in appearance. They form where sea waters are agitated by waves or tides and where there is strong evaporation, as in parts of the Caribbean today. Each round fragment, or *ooid*, has a microscopic nucleus of a skeletal fragment or pellet around which concentric layers of calcium carbonate have grown. Both the rounded shape and the polish on the surface are caused by the movement of the particles in the water currents. Gradually the *ooids* accumulated on the sea floor and over time became compacted and cemented together to form the rock we see today. You can often see the remains of sea shells amongst the *ooids*. We call this stone oolitic limestone or oolite.

Sections of (a) uncemented oolite and (b) cemented Bath Stone (both x24)

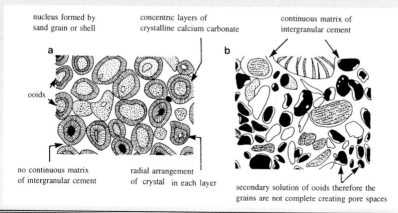

nucleus formed by sand grain or shell

concentric layers of crystalline calcium carbonate

continuous matrix of intergranular cement

ooids

no continuous matrix of intergranular cement

radial arrangement of crystal in each layer

secondary solution of ooids therefore the grains are not complete creating pore spaces

Continental collisions

About 25 million years ago, when Africa moved north, colliding with the continent of Europe, the mountain chains of southern Europe were formed. A distant effect of these violent earth movements was the tilting of the Jurassic beds of Britain to the south-east. You can see the edge of these Jurassic rocks from Portland and Purbeck in Dorset, through Bath and the Cotswolds, Northamptonshire and Lincolnshire to the North York Moors. Good building stones occur at many places along this Jurassic outcrop.

Local exposure by river erosion

The manner in which the River Avon has cut through the south-east sloping Jurassic rocks of the Bath area is the key to the way Bath Stone has been worked at various localities. Around the city itself, the stone beds are high on the hill tops giving them their plateau-like character and close enough to the surface to be obtained from open-cast pits, for example at Combe Down and Odd Down. The Romans worked these areas in quarries and in shallow mines. Further up the valley of the Avon, to the east, the valuable building material lies a little below hilltop level around Monkton Farleigh, Conkwell, Winsley and Box. In these districts the Avon valley provided many hillside exposures and where the quality was good, as at Box, mining followed the quarrying so the beds were pursued under the hilltop capping.

Characteristics of Bath Stone

Bath Stone, being a sedimentary rock deposited in layers on the sea bed, has a natural layering or bedding. It also has natural vertical fractures or joints caused by later earth movements. A major feature of the stone is that it is a freestone, i.e. one which can be sawn up or squared in any direction. While the joints do not greatly affect the use of the stone, except in limiting the size of individual blocks, the bedding most certainly does. To obtain satisfactory results and wear, the *Bath Stone* must be "laid on its bed", that is, as it was in the ground. If it is not laid in this way, the layers tend to peel off as a result of weathering.

The stone does vary in quality according to its exact location. All types will carve with great precision but some are more durable than others. For example, Box Ground Stone and Westwood Stone are preferred for detailed work while that from Monk's Park is used mostly for plain ashlar (sawn) blocks and is rarely carved as it weathers relatively quickly.

As you face the south wall of the Abbey, walk a few metres to your right to the entrance of the Abbey Heritage Vaults.

Outside the entrance is a Millennium carving, 'The Resurrection of Christ'. This life-sized figure was carved by Laurence Tindall from three blocks of *Bath Stone* from local stone mined at Limpley Stoke. It is an excellent example of the beauty of the stone and how well it can be carved.

Now return to the Abbey Church Yard and look at the stones which pave the open courtyard.

Another local stone

The dark grey paving stones here are made of **Pennant Sandstone** (information box, page 8). About 320 million years ago, rivers flowing from high land to the north deposited sand in river deltas. These covered a wide area including present day Bristol. Over time, this sand, consisting mainly of quartz grains, became the *Pennant Sandstone.* Between Bath and Bristol, the River Avon cuts a gorge through this sandstone, making quarrying and river transport easy. Some beds are thin, so suitable for pavings, while others are thick and used as blocks for building.

How to attract a crowd

You will need to inspect these pavings quite closely and you will probably attract a crowd of curious people. This sandstone weathers quite quickly and then puddles form on it. To allow the water to drain away and to give a better grip, many

of the flags here have been scored with strong corrugations.

This is called bunching. You can see where some of them have weathered as small flakes are breaking away. Some of the smaller, parallel grooves across the slabs are caused by abrasion from the wire used in cutting. It is possible to see curved lines too. These are eroded ripple marks - imagine the ripples that you walk across when you paddle in the sea being cut off flat.

On the west side of the courtyard is the wall of the Roman Baths.

The ashlar blocks here have bevelled edges, giving recessed joints. Sinking the joints in stonework is called rustication. It creates shadows which give the stonework a more massive appearance. When only the horizontal joints are sunk, it is known as banded rustication. On top of this wall is a Victorian balustraded terrace above the Great Bath, with statues of Roman emperors and governors (sculpted by George Lawson in 1894).

The stone of the projecting sections of the wall has been deeply gouged to give a coarse surface texture of ridges and hollows. This kind of decoration is called vermiculation because the pattern of the ridges resembles worm tracks. At balustrade level the projecting blocks have been pitted by circular drilled or chiselled holes of various sizes. This is another form of vermiculation. Vermiculation is often used together with rustication to give an appearance of greater weight. The west side of the Pump Room, seen later, shows a good example of this.

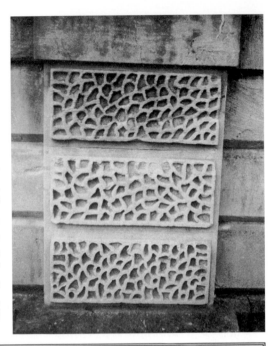

Pennant and Paving

During Georgian times, *Pennant Sandstone* was the preferred stone for footways and paved pedestrian areas. It later became used for outside steps, as column bases, for the lower courses of walls and for setts which are the stone blocks used to surface carriageways. Setts have an average top surface of 25cm x 14cm but the size varies greatly. Modern setts are usually about 11cm square.

Prior to this time, paving was in oolitic limestone from the surrounding hills and **Blue** or **White Lias** limestone from quarries mainly in Lower Weston and Twerton to the west of the city. By the third quarter of the sixteenth century, paving was commonplace in nearly every street and lane in the city and suburbs. 'Paving' here means 'pitching', that is, small square blocks packed together to form a solid surface. Posts separated footway and carriageway. The following was recorded in the diary of Celia Fiennes, on or before 1687. *"The streets of a good size and well pitched and cleane kept"*.

Limestone flagstones were used for "paved walks", the first being laid down in 1705 at the present-day Orange Grove. Flags are rectangular slabs of stone in a variety of sizes.

A popular stone for footways

In the early 1730s, *Pennant Sandstone* was chosen to repair Abbey Church Yard and ten years later John Wood specified *Pennant Sandstone* for the surfacing of the parades, although limestone was still used for less important areas. From then on, *Pennant Sandstone* gained in popularity and by the early nineteenth century, all streets with definite footways were in *Pennant Sandstone*. It was not used for carriageways however, until 1830, being considered too valuable. During the eighteenth century both footways and carriageways were bedded on a rubble core of re-used waste stone, fresh oolitic limestone rubble or Pleistocene sand and gravel from the River Avon. In the nineteenth century these were replaced by concrete.

The iron-shod wooden wagon wheels caused both a high noise level and major erosion of the limestone carriageways. This created large volumes of dust and watering the streets to settle the dust was an on-going problem. This finally led to a ban on four-horse teams entering the city and with them the slow, heavy carts that did most of the damage. This is an early example of traffic control, a problem with which Bath still wrestles!

Experimental road surfaces

The nineteenth century saw many experiments in an attempt to reduce wear and tear on the roads. Of these, Clee Hill Dhu *dolerite* setts (now used in the wall at Abbey Church House) and granite kerbs will be seen on the walks. The mid-nineteenth century saw wooden blocks laid on sand, sealed with tarmac pitch, which proved quiet but very expensive. Macadamising was also tried. This consisted of small 5cm square blocks which compact under pressure. Many different types of stone were used. This process later became tar-macadamising, hence tarmac. Glazed brick was to be found on the horse stands where washing-down facilities were available. Today concrete slabs have spread across many of the footways and only isolated carriageways are still surfaced with setts, the Royal Crescent, seen later in the walk, being the most notable.

Although there are plenty of other different building stones used within the city, the two most common stones have now been introduced. You should be able to recognise plenty of examples throughout the walk.

Leaving the south part of the Abbey Church Yard, now walk to the west front of the Abbey.

Bath Abbey

The existing building is on the site of a Norman Abbey which was itself built over a Saxon predecessor. It is Perpendicular Gothic in style and was begun in 1499 but not completed in its present form until the nineteenth century. A leading architect of the Victorian Gothic revival, Sir George Gilbert Scott (Albert Memorial, St Pancras Station Hotel), was responsible for the final additions and much restorative work.

If you look inside the Abbey, you will see the soaring fan-vaulted stone roof of the nave. This was designed by Scott in the style of the sixteenth century ceiling of the chancel, and only completed in 1876. It replaced a lath and plaster ceiling built in the time of James I and so the Gothic edifice, begun in 1499, was effectively finished 377 years on.

On the west front of the Abbey (see below), notice again how well *Bath Stone* can be carved. On either side of the great west window are 16th century sculptures of the dream ladder seen by Bishop Oliver King, who instigated the building following his famous dream.

He dreamed about the Holy Trinity and a ladder with angels ascending and descending. To the left and right on the outermost buttresses are crowned olive trees below a mitre. This was a play on the name of the bishop. The central figure above the door is the reigning monarch, Henry VII.

Although a beautiful building stone, *Bath Stone* does suffer quite badly from weathering, i.e. the effects of the weather erode the stone. Compare some of the restored figures on the west front with those that have not been restored.

Caithness Flags

Looking at the ground in the yard in front of the west front of the Abbey you will recognise that most of the flagstones here are of the same *Pennant Sandstone* seen earlier but there are also some very large darker flags which come from *Caithness* in the far north of Scotland. This stone formed about 370 million years ago in a temporary lake in a desert area (a playa). Deposits were laid down repeatedly in the lake whenever water was present (cyclical deposition).

If you imagine the mud after the lake has evaporated, you would expect to see desiccation, or drying-out, cracks and mud patterning, wouldn't you? In fact these ancient desiccation marks are visible on these flagstones too. It's often true in geology that if you understand what is happening in the environment today, then you can understand what you see in rocks which formed millions of years ago. These flagstones are Devonian in age (page 46) and are famous for their durability. They were almost certainly transported from Caithness to Bristol by sea and so to Bath.

Snail creep

It is fascinating that so many of the stones around us display evidence indicating the history of their formation and evolution. If you have time, you might like to look for another indicator.

In the wall opposite the south-west corner of the Abbey are examples of 'snail creep'. 'Snail creep' is a quarryman's term for the thin, nearly vertical pale lines in some of the stone blocks. The rock split as it was forming and calcite was deposited from water which flowed through these joints.

Continue westwards across Abbey Church Yard. On your left before you reach the colonnade are the entrances to the Roman Baths and Pump Room, both built from Bath Stone. You may pass through the doors to view the entrance hall.

Bath Spa Water

Bath has long been famous for its natural spa water, rich in minerals and used for the treatment of a wide range of ailments for centuries. Mesolithic implements provide evidence for the earliest known human occupation of Bath hot springs about 7000 years ago. Evidence of Iron Age use of the springs is also substantial, although no large structures were built around the springs until an early date in the Roman occupation, possibly about 60AD. This marks the first appearance of Bath as a spa and it survived in this form until the 5th century. The hot springs were still active in the Dark Ages and the springs were restored in the 7th century and continued in use until the 1970s.

When National Health Service funding was withdrawn in 1975 all the spa facilities were closed. One swimming bath using the springs remained in use but that too closed in 1978 because of suspected contamination of the thermal water. Now a new spa facility and treatment centre is being built as a Millennium project.

The highest surface groundwater temperatures in the United Kingdom are found at Bath where the springs have constant temperatures of 41^0 - 47^0C at ground level. For many years it was thought that the hot water in Bath was derived from the Mendip Hills in Somerset but its passage from here was always difficult to explain. Recent research has suggested the Bath's hot springs are related to the Avon-Solent fracture zone. The hot springs of Bristol and Bath and two geothermal wells at Southampton are located on a 155 km long fracture zone extending in a north-west to south-east direction from the Severn Estuary to the English Channel. Initiated during mountain building caused by all the continents joining together, about 200 million years ago, and reactivated about 40 million years ago with the building of the Alps, the structure, which extends across the English Channel into France, is still active.

The following is an extract from the diary of Celia Fiennes, circa 1687,

"it is very hot and tastes like the water that boyles eggs,
has such a smell, but nearer the pumpe you drinke it
the hotter and less offencive and more spiriteous."

Roman Baths and the Pump Room

The Roman Baths

Inside the entrance to the Roman Baths, the floor is of polished white, black and red blocks:-

❑ **WHITE** is *Carrara marble* which has fine blue-grey veins in it. Originally this was a slightly muddy limestone which was changed (metamorphosed) by heat and pressure into a marble. The clay minerals from the mud make the blue-grey veins.

❑ **BLACK** blocks are Carboniferous limestone from Belgium, (timescale, page 46). The black colour indicates that this limestone formed in a rather murky environment with very little oxygen present (anaerobic).

❑ **RED** blocks are limestone from the Mediterranean, Spain or Portugal. It formed in a shallow sea where there were many bivalves. Most here are rudist bivalves which have a distinctive ice-cream Cone shape.

Also, note the pillars of Devonian marble with many shatter cracks filled with pink and white calcite. The collision of two continents caused mountain building, which in turn caused the limestone to become marble and caused the tension cracks. The red staining was caused by the desertification of the landscape after the mountain building.

The two beautiful statues to the right of the entrance are made from white *Carrara marble* on **serpentinite / gabbro** bases. Serpentinite is an altered igneous rock and *gabbro* is a coarse-grained igneous rock rich in iron and magnesium. Opinions differ about whether the rock is *Serpentinite* or *gabbro*.

The Pump Room

The building which is next on your left is the Pump Room, started by Thomas Baldwin and completed by John Palmer in the 1790s. The fact that *Bath Stone* carves easily and beautifully can again be seen in the Corinthian columns and in the oak leaves and acorns which adorn the pediment. The Greek inscription below the pediment informs visitors that 'water is best'. Oak leaves and acorns are used because of the story of Bladud and the pigs (page 2).

The copings here are covered in lead which was always used as weather protection in high quality building work. Lead was available from the Mendip Hills where the mines were still working into the nineteenth century.

You will see that the bases of the *Bath Stone* columns here are made from the *Pennant Sandstone*. This is a much more durable stone and does not weather as badly as *Bath Stone* would in these circumstances. Can you see the places where the *Bath Stone* has weathered?

Now pass through the colonnade into Stall Street, turn left and walk a few metres into the open space in front of the King's and Queen's Bath. The hanging sign reads 'The Pump Room'; this is its west side (see above).

Note the vermiculation in the *Bath Stone* as you walk along this side of the Pump Room. Also notice the beautifully designed setts. Here these are made of the hard igneous rock, ***granite*** (page 43). This granite is from Portugal and is about 250 million years old, the same age as Cornish granite. Portugal and, more recently, China, are now the cheapest sources of this material.

The bronze UNESCO logo in the centre of the road and the plaque on the railing in front of the Pump Room mark the City of Bath as a World Heritage Site.

A fountain once stood in this open space where the people of Bath could sample the Spa water. On top of the fountain was a statue of Bladud carved by Pieroni in 1859. The fountain can now be seen in Terrace Walk to where it was resited in 1988 (seen later in the walk).

Look south, down Stall Street. The tree-covered hills, facing you; form a river cliff cut by the River Avon.

From the front of the King's and Queen's Bath, looking west is Bath Street, a colonnaded walkway designed by Baldwin in 1789 and built 1791-4.

The Green Southern Loop

A short additional diversion (see the Green route on the rear cover map) begins here. It examines in more detail the use of stone on modern shop fronts and adds about 500m to the City Centre walk. If you elect to do the southern loop now, or later, you will find directions on page 39. The 'green' southern loop rejoins the main 'yellow' walk in Bath Street (see below).

Continue the main, yellow, City Centre walk by walking along Bath Street towards the Cross Bath, facing you at the end of the street (see photo above).

Bath Street

Bath Street connects the baths in Stall Street with the Cross Bath. Although most of the columns in Bath Street are made of *Bath Stone* in cylindrical blocks, up to one metre in length, some may be concrete replacements with thin limestone cladding, while others are painted or stuccoed. Stucco is a plaster of lime and fine sand. The buildings of Bath Street are deceptive in that the *Bath Stone* is thin, acting only as a cladding on a timber frame construction.

The Cross Bath

At the end of Bath Street, the Cross Bath, facing you, and the adjacent Hot Bath, on the left, like the other buildings around you, are all built of *Bath Stone*.

The Cross Bath was designed by Baldwin, 1784, as a terminal feature for his new Bath Street. The details carved in the stone here are excellent. It was built on the site of a cross erected to commemorate the visit in 1687 of Mary, second wife of James II. At that time, none of her five children had survived and she had had several miscarriages. She took the waters and in 1688, James Francis Edward Stuart, the Old Pretender, was born. This did no harm at all to Bath's reputation!

In the seventeenth century, the Cross Bath was definitely 'up market'. On Monday 15th June 1668, Samuel Pepys recorded -

'Looked into the Baths and find the King and Queenes full of a mixed sort of good and bad, and the Cross only for the gentry.'

The Hot Bath was designed by John Wood the Younger and built from 1775-8. It was the only public building this famous architect was commissioned to design in Bath.

Both the Cross Bath and the Hot Bath have been restored and incorporated into the new spa facility for the Millennium.

Continue by turning left between the Cross Bath, on your right and the Hot Bath on your left, and into Hetling Court.

Hetling Court

The base of the building, about 15m on your right, the back of St John's Hospital, uses **slaty tuff** as a protective ground-level cladding. This is a very interesting rock formed in the Lake District, about 475 million years ago from ash thrown out from one of the greatest *volcanic* eruptions ever to take place in Britain. If you look closely you can see *volcanic* fragments which chilled quickly as they landed.

This metamorphosed volcanic extrusive rock (see pages 44 and 45) is used here because it is durable. You can see that in this low damp position it is better than *Bath Stone* by comparing the two together further along the alley-way. This volcanic cladding was added when this part of the hospital complex was restored and rebuilt in the 1960s. The Hospital was built by the Bishop of Bath and Wells in the late 12th century to enable the poor and sick of the city to benefit from the hot waters.

At the end of Hetling Court, looking back, St John's Hospital is now on the left. It is roofed with stone tiles. Note the carved Bishop's mitres, a reference to the founder, on the tops of the gable ends.

Roofing Materials

Stone tiles

The roof of St John's hospital is a rare example of the original style of roofing, only seen today in the city on buildings pre-dating the Georgian growth. Stone tiles, the traditional roofing material, are still commonly seen in Cotswold villages to the north of the city. They were made from thin slabs of limestone which were graded from the largest at the eaves to the smallest near the ridge and are laid traditionally at just over 50 degrees. They are very heavy and old roofs covered with stone tiles can usually be observed to be sagging somewhat between supports.

The grading is a matter of achieving sufficient lap to exclude the water – more of it at the bottom of the slope. Although the top tiles are smaller, there are more laps, so the weight hardly varies. The pitch arises from a vertical:horizontal ratio of 4:3. These roofs need a steep pitch because of the gaps between tiles, but beyond 50 degrees, wind forces increase fast.

Slates and terracotta tiles

In the city, the shallower Georgian roofs which replaced the stone tiles are normally covered with *slate* or terracotta tiles, commonly with *slate* on the front and clay tiles on the inner, invisible slopes. The slates come from Cornwall and Wales, the most common sizes being 24ins x 12ins ('princesses') and 20ins x 10ins ('duchesses').

The terracotta are mostly 'Patent Double Roman' and were a speciality of Bridgwater, Somerset. Locally they are sometimes called 'Bridgwaters'.

Slates and stone tiles are laid 'double lap' i.e. they lap over the top of the slate or tile two courses below. This is because water can enter at the sides. Bridgwater tiles have a waterproof lateral overlap, or sidelock, so can be laid to a single lap vertically. This makes them light and economical. They were the precursor of the modern interlocking concrete tile. Pantiles, more common in other parts of the country, were sometimes used, as in Beauford Square, seen later on the walk.

Chimney Pots

Traditional chimney pots in Bath were square and made of *Bath Stone*. They weathered badly and virtually all have been replaced by terracotta in a wide variety of styles. One house in Duke Street, off North Parade, has been restored with square chimneys.

At the end of Hetling Court turn left to examine Abbey Church House, almost immediately on your left opposite the roundabout.

Abbey Church House

The original building was a leper hospital in 1136. The present house was built for Edward Clarke in 1570 and restored after bombing in 1942. It is virtually the only remnant of Elizabethan Bath. Look at the building stone facing used in this house. The blocks of its walls are mostly oolitic limestone (*Bath Stone*) but a variety of other rocks was incorporated during post World War II rebuilding.

Between the left of the door and the left bay window are several rectangular blocks paler than the cream limestone around them. These are *White Lias* Limestone formed from a lime-rich mud in a very shallow, low-energy sea. Some of the limestone blocks in the wall have been reddened by fire.

Towards the left end of the front wall (see photo below) are three black volcanic rocks with a fourth much higher up. These are Clee Hill Dhu, an olivine-*dolerite* from the Welsh Borders. These igneous rocks were brought to Bath as part of street surfacing experiments in the nineteenth century (see page 9). The stones seen here are the right size to have been originally cut as setts.

Look at the building on the opposite side of the road to the entrance to Hetling Court (14 Westgate Buildings). Again, you can see that ashlar blocks have been used at the front, but rough hewn stone is used for the side.

Returning to the end of Hetling Court, walk a few metres beyond to enter Chapel Court through the iron gate on your right and walk through into the courtyard (the gate is locked at 10.30 p.m.).

Chapel Court

On your right and ahead are the buildings of St John's Hospital, a charitable institution established in 1174. The arcaded building in front of you and its neighbour on the left, Chapel Court House, together with the adjacent Chandos Buildings, were the first significant designs of John Wood (1704-1754), the young

himself (now known as Chandos Buildings), new almshouses and lodgings for visitors to the Cross Bath. The hospital was restored in 1877-8 and again in 1969. It is yet another good example of *Bath Stone*. Notice that the inset carving of the lamb above the doorway and the two blocks on either side are made of a white limestone. This is *Portland Stone* from Dorset.

Mortar match

You will notice, as elsewhere in Bath, the mortar between the blocks here is very well chosen and matches the texture and the colour of *Bath Stone*. Ashlar was bedded in 'mason's putty', made from lime plus stone dust with a very little sand. Contrast this with the gross ribbon pointing on the wall on your right as you return to the road. It is the wrong colour, is too hard and is non-porous - not a good choice between porous blocks of *Bath Stone*.

architect who pioneered Bath's great Georgian golden age of building (see Queen Square, visited later). Erected in 1727/8, these buildings are an outstanding example of the harmony of Wood's classical designs and the clean lines of the *Bath Stone*. Chapel Court has *Pennant Sandstone* paving in the centre.

In the 1720s the Duke of Chandos, who had stayed in lodgings above the almshouses, decided to rebuild the whole layout as a Close, complete with a town house for

Return through the gate and turn right along Westgate Buildings.

Westgate Buildings

As you walk north, the City of Bath College is on the left. It uses the same green, *slaty tuff* seen in Hetling Court. The window here often has a display of students' stonemasonry work.

Opposite the College (30-32 Westgate Buildings) is Rosenberg House, a former part of the hospital, now rebuilt (1975). This again has ground level cladding of green, *slaty tuff*.

At the end of Westgate Buildings, turn left for a brief diversion into Kingsmead Square.

Kingsmead Square

On the right (west side), look for No 14 Rosewell House, (J. Strahan 1735). Each doorway column is in two, one-metre segments of oolitic limestone. The bedding, laid horizontally, as it should be, is shown by discontinuous layers of finely-ground shell fragments. Note the wonderful Baroque decorations on this building, unique in Bath.

Kingsmead Square is paved with re-used *Pennant Sandstone* slabs, some of which have grooves in, originally for carrying water away. A good example of one of these can be seen near the plane tree on the pavement between Monmouth Street and Kingsmead Square, close to the Monmouth Street kerb.

Now return to the end of Westgate Buildings and crossing the end of Westgate Street begin to climb Saw Close.

A few metres up the hill on the left is Seven Dials (the new building of Bath Stone on the corner).

Seven Dials

Built on the site of Kingsmead Fields outside the West Gate of the City, this building is a good example of a sympathetic modern replica of the Georgian building style with smooth-finish ashlar blocks of beautiful *Bath Stone* being used. The building stone is from Stoke Hill Mine at Limpley Stoke; it is 'Stoke Ground *Bath Stone*'. This is one of the best places on the walk to see fresh oolitic limestone.

Look carefully at the pillars at the southern (downhill) end, and you will see lots of crescent-shaped sea shell cross-sections and lines that indicate the direction of the marine currents. On the back of the second pillar up, at about adult eye-level, there is a cluster of brachiopod shells, as shown in the small photo on the rear cover.

Why are the shells in a little group? Brachiopods lived attached to the sea bed by a fleshy stalk. Perhaps they were killed by storm waves which covered them in the tiny ooids? Then their insides could have rotted away and that is how they became filled with the same sediment as around them. Very coarse oolite is used for the column plinths and some have large cavities. Perhaps these were worm burrows? Beyond the Seven Dials is No 10 Saw Close, The Garrick's Head, which is an early Georgian house, once the home of Beau Nash.

20

Continue to walk on the left side of the road, passing the Theatre Royal.

A few metres beyond, partly obscured by the Theatre's protruding foyer, is the beautiful entrance to the house of Beau Nash's mistress, Juliana Popjoy (hence 'Popjoy's Restaurant'). This is another excellent example of how well the *Bath Stone* can be carved.

40m beyond the Theatre, pause, opposite Trim Street, before turning left into Beauford Square.

Volcanic bombs

On either side of the road into Beauford Square, are modern buildings with *Bath Stone* facings on the second and third storeys.

The ground floor shop fronts are clad in green *slaty tuff*. If you were interested in this volcanic material before, then cross the road and look closely at the second block up from the pavement to the right of the door. There is a marked scour structure in the volcanic ash. This is where a water channel was cut in the ash and then this was infilled with another layer of pyroclastic material. You can even see volcanic bombs here!

Beauford Square

On the right (north side) of the square is one of Georgian Bath's early small-scale domestic developments. It was built in the late 1720s, about the same time as Queen Square, to designs of the Bristol architect, John Strahan.

Notice the roofs on the north side -

numbers 15 and 16 combine Roman and flat tiles whereas numbers 19 and 20 combine pantiles and flat tiles. *Slate* is used on either side (see Roofing Materials, page 17). When numbers 15 to 20 were restored in 1981, the following report appeared on 26th September in the Bath Chronicle, 'Scratched on a window of number 16 with a diamond was –

"God gave us light and it was good
Pitt came and taxed it -
Damn his blood".'

The window above the door of No 20, blocked in to avoid the window tax referred to in the lines above, shows evidence of subsidence. The north side of the Theatre Royal can also be seen from this Square. This was designed by the architect George Dance the Younger, and the foundation stone was laid in 1804. The ground floor has been altered subsequently; the original front entrance was here.

Return towards the front of the theatre and Popjoy's crossing the road into Upper Borough Walls, pass along Upper Borough Walk to the junction with Trim Bridge.

Upper Borough Walls

The street names here have been cut into *Bath Stone* using beautiful Roman capitals. You will see further examples on this walk. The initials are Parish boundaries:

S.M.P.　　= St Michael's Parish
S.P.P.P.　= Abbey Church of St Peter with St Paul's Parish and 'St James' (added when the church was bombed in W.W.II).

Now walk about 15m further along Upper Borough Walls.

The wall along the left (north side) is said to be part of the medieval wall of the City. It is built of a great variety of rocks some of which you will have seen before. Look for a curved shell of a bivalve called the Devil's Toe-nail *(Gryphaea).* There are also good examples of cross bedding, (see page 31). Can you also see some rocks with holes in? These are burrows made by bivalves, oyster-like creatures.

Bodies from the hospital behind you were taken over this wall for burial as explained on the plaque which can be seen on the left if you look through the gap in the parapet of the wall.

On the opposite side of the street, high on the wall of the Mineral Water Hospital, is a life-size sculpture of the Good Samaritan, complete with donkey. This is another example of the superb carving quality of *Bath Stone.*

Continue along Upper Borough Walls and take the first left down the lane at the end of the wall.

Burrows　??
Of course they are Burrows.
These are the Upper Burrow Walls.

You are walking down into the old ditch around the city wall.

The setts here show a very good example of 'bunching' (page 7).

Turn left at the end of this short lane into Trim Street.

Trim Street

Note the house on the left hand corner at the beginning of Trim Street. There are heavy wooden beams along two of the walls above the windows and they are dovetailed at the corner of the street. This was sometimes used as an alternative to *Bath Stone* lintels.

About 10m from this corner, in the road, there are *Pennant Sandstone* paving slabs which covered the entrances to coal holes in cellars beneath. You will see one of these slabs in the road with a hole in it. The slabs originally had a metal pull which the coalmen used to pull them up.

No 5 Trim Street is General Wolfe's House, built about 1720. It is an early example of building in the Palladian style in Bath.

Turn right under the arch into Queen Street.

Queen Street

As you walk under the archway here, note the setts. In some places, beyond the arch, *Pennant Sandstone* has been replaced by *Blue Lias* limestone with very clear, beautiful fossils; mostly the bivalve *Gryphaea*. You can see that the *Blue Lias* limestone has polished much more than the *Pennant Sandstone* and so does not give such a good grip.

About 15m up on the right, two widths of kerb have been used and the *Pennant Sandstone* flags in the pavement, at the right-hand, top corner of the road, are cut on a radius.

What's in a name?

At the staggered cross-roads at the end of Queen Street, notice the road names - John Street, Wood Street and Quiet Street. It is said that at a meeting to decide street names, John Wood was being very awkward and argumentative. When there were only three streets left to name, the exasperated Mayor shouted, 'John Wood - quiet!' If this story is true, it is delightful; if not, then it's still a good story!

Turn left here into Wood Street and proceed to Queen Square.

Queen Square

This was built between 1728 and 1736 and was John Wood the Elder's first major development in Bath. Wood believed that the proportions of classical architecture were divinely inspired and that noble buildings could serve as a moral corrective. They were not to be regarded as merely an imposing framework for everyday life.

Using Roman and Palladian principles, he designed a city where the houses were not jumbled but joined in graceful terraces, crescents and squares, all using the beautiful, cream *Bath Stone*. No other English city shows such a combination of magnificent design with decorative splendour.

The north front of Queen Square is the showpiece, with seven large houses forming a symmetrical composition, with three-quarter pilasters and columns, an attic storey and large central pediment.

Walk around the square in a clockwise direction to the west side of the Square.

The central part of the west front is not by John Wood but is an 1830 addition in the Greek revival style. It occupies what was originally an open space in front of a set-back house. 16 Queen Square, part of this addition, is now the headquarters of the BRLSI (Bath Royal Literary and Scientific Institute). The Bath Geological Society meets here once a month. A contact name is at the back of this booklet.

The Obelisk in the centre of the Square is built of *Bath Stone* and was erected by Nash in 1738 in honour of Frederick, Prince of Wales' visit to Bath. It has been reduced in size.

Conservation of buildings

In Bath there is continuing conflict between those who think that the buildings should display all the characteristics of their original architecture and those who think they should reflect changes over time. The building on the north-west corner of Queen Square engenders much strong feeling. Should the walls and windows be covered in creeper or kept as originally built?

Similarly many Georgian buildings that you will see on the walk have Victorian plate glass windows, whereas others have either original or restored glazing bars. Many first-floor windows have been lengthened, and some restored to their original size. The surrounding stonework often shows the effect of both alteration and restoration of windows. You can see this in the houses at the south end of both the western and the eastern sides of Queen Square.

Walk north up the west side of Queen Square, cross the road, Queen Square Place, and walk straight ahead up Queen's Parade towards Victoria Park.

On the first building on your right, after you have crossed the road, note the small granite columns, each made from a single piece. This is **Peterhead Granite** from Aberdeenshire in Scotland.

Heathens

If you look closely at the granite you will see small pieces of black rock in amongst the crystals. These represent the original Grampian schist material into which the granitic magma intruded. They were not completely assimilated before crystallisation occurred. They are called xenoliths but the old quarrymen used to call them 'heathens', i.e. not acceptable in the granite. Some of the 'heathens' have little feldspars beginning to grow in them; they were known as converted 'heathens'; a reflection of 19th century attitudes.

Granite kerbstones

Just before you cross the road into Victoria Park, notice the kerbstones. They are made from **Cornish Granite** and contain very large white feldspar crystals. These crystallised first in the magma and so grew slowly to a great size and then the rest of the magma cooled and crystallised with smaller crystals surrounding the large feldspars.

Continue towards Victoria Park, keeping to the path on the left.

The War Memorial, the Cross of Remembrance, on your left, is made of *Portland Stone*. This is known as pin-head oolite; the ooids are smaller than in *Bath Stone* (page 5) and so are more difficult to see without a hand lens. You can see some oyster shells in the rock.

The two magnificent stone lions at the entrance to the park are made of Coade Stone. This is not a natural stone but a fired clay that was produced in London between about 1770 and 1840.

Victoria Park

Just inside the entrance is the locally famous 'Miller' Vase. Lady Miller, a famous eccentric from Bath, bought a Roman Vase in Frascati in Italy, while on the grand tour. There is some speculation whether this vase is indeed the one from Italy but it is made of white marble so it could indeed be the original vase.

Pause to the left of the Miller vase, where a pathway leads off towards the Bowling Green.

The low *Bath Stone* walls on each side of this path have a row of holes drilled in the top. These were to take metal railings. Some stumps can be seen on the right hand side. In the early days of World War II, railings were declared a strategic war material and they were removed wholesale. This was a great cultural loss, especially of Victorian ironwork. Railings were only spared on safety grounds so the deep, open basements of Georgian buildings kept theirs. You will see these on the next part of the walk.

Continue on the main path up the hill past the Park Pavilion on your left, until you see a huge flower urn on the other side of the road.

This urn, made of *Bath Stone*, was carved by Pieroni who also carved Bladud for the fountain which once stood in Stall Street.

Now leave the Royal Avenue and take the path north, to the left of the urn, walking uphill towards the Royal Crescent.

On the right, where the Park ends, is a wide footpath with garden walls to the left. This is 'Gravel Walk' and was once the route used by sedan chairs to and from the Royal Crescent.

Continue up to the end of the lane and turn left into the Royal Crescent.

The Royal Crescent

This crescent of thirty houses was built between 1767 and 1775 of *Bath Stone* and was designed by

John Wood the Younger (1721-1781). It was the first crescent built in England and has an elliptical, not circular curvature. It is a truly magnificent sight with its great sweep of over one hundred Ionic columns embracing the first and second floors.

The wide pavement (above) is constructed from *Pennant Sandstone* and the roadway is also mostly *Pennant Sandstone* setts (photo right) with a few replacements, for example, opposite No 9 there are setts of *granite* and *dolerite*.

Return to the top of the path you climbed from Victoria Park. Continue ahead into Brock Street.

Brock Street

As you can see, all the buildings around this area are built of *Bath Stone*. About 25m on your right is a Gothic door which is the only remaining part of Lady Margaret Chapel (1772-3). Like the Royal Crescent, it was designed by John Wood the Younger who was also responsible for Brock Street itself (1764-70).

Margaret's Buildings

About 50m down Brock Street on your left is Margaret's Buildings. This delightful and interesting pedestrian precinct frames the tower of St Stephen's Church in the distance (right).

Continue along Brock Street to The Circus. Walk anticlockwise, right, around the Circus pausing on the far side (Nos 19-21).

The Circus

The Circus was built between 1754 and 1758 and is John Wood the Elder's architectural masterpiece. It is built of *Bath Stone*. Wood may have drawn inspiration from Stonehenge and the Colosseum in Rome. Here there are Greek columns of all three orders on top of each other, Doric at ground level, then Ionic then Corinthian (see front cover).

The frieze between the ground and first floor of these buildings is carved with a succession of emblems of arts, sciences and trades, almost without repetition.

Continue around the Circus until turning right into Bennett Street. After 25m you will see the Assembly Rooms on your right.

The tools of the stone mason are included. No 30 has a replacement block (1962) showing a mallet, chisel and calipers and No 21 (top right) has a stone saw, similar to those used to cut the ashlar blocks of these buildings.

Architecture, carpentry and metal-working are all represented. The parapet is adorned with 108 stone acorns, perhaps to commemorate the Bladud legend.

The plane trees in the centre, planted 200 years ago, hide a reservoir which, being raised above the level of the basement kitchens, provided water to the houses by gravity feed.

Bath at Work

'Bath at Work' is an industrial heritage centre, which you may like to visit at some time. It is only a short walk from here. If you decide to visit it now, walk up Russell Street (see map), turning sharp right into Rivers Street, then left into Julian Road. The museum then faces you across the road. The location is also shown on the rear cover map. If you visit this museum, you will find amongst the many interesting exhibits, a reconstruction of a *Bath Stone* quarry face.

After turning right pause in front of the Assembly Rooms on your left.

The Assembly Rooms (1768 - 81) were designed by John Wood the Younger. This area was badly damaged in World War II and restored in the post-war years.

From here, note the back of the houses of The Circus, on your right. Many of the additions to the rear of Georgian houses started life as small wooden box-like structures attached to the outside of the stonework at various levels. These were used as lavatories to replace the curtained alcove with chamber pot common in even the most elegant rooms. Time and weather made many of these structures unsound, sometimes leading to a spectacular collapse whilst still occupied!

Alfred Street

Continue across the front of the Assembly Rooms to Alfred Street.

In front of you is No 14, Alfred House. Behind the railings, notice a winch. This was used to raise and lower items such as kitchen supplies and also the family sedan chair if stored in the basement. On either side of the entrance are cone-shaped snuffers used to extinguish the torches carried by footmen.

Turn left into Alfred Street and continue to where Saville Row rises to your left and Bartlett Street drops steeply on the right, to the south.

Looking down Bartlett Street the view ahead to the southern hills allows one to appreciate the statement that 'Bath is in a green bowl'. Only to the west is there an easy way in or out.

Facing the hills to the south, start walking down Bartlett Street.

Cladding

In new buildings of commercial type, it is common nowadays to place a thin, decorative stone skin, or cladding, attached to the outside of the load-bearing structural frame which is generally of concrete or steel. In Bath, such stone cladding is very widespread and is of two main types:

❑ natural *Bath Stone*, to blend in with the older buildings,
❑ brought in from elsewhere (often abroad) to provide durability and an attractive appearance to the front of a building.

Imported cladding stones are generally finished to a glossy, polished external surface. The most common ones are explained in the Glossary of Rock Names, pages 43-44. Examples of most of these cladding materials can be seen in any High Street in Britain and Bath is no exception.

Bartlett Street

The shop, 'House of Bath', on the right, has a cladding of coarse *granite* with pink feldspars and pale grey quartz. The Corinthian capitals and bases are made of **New Red Sandstone**, possibly from south-west Scotland and is Permo-Triassic in age (page 46). There is also a beautiful *New Red Sandstone* arch over the main entrance with a limestone pediment above (see below).

At Nos 5 and 6, on the opposite side of the street, is a cladding of granite with some of the quartz coloured dark red. This is *Peterhead Granite* again and has some 'heathens' (page 24). Between Nos 6 and 7, the column bases are of *New Red Sandstone* on a plinth of greenish-grey *Pennant Sandstone*. The base of the House of Bath is clad in dark 'emerald pearl' **larvikite**.

Continue to the bottom of Bartlett Street to George Street. Cross the road, turn right and then left into Milsom Street.

The Building of Bath Museum

This museum tells the story of the buildings of Bath; how they were designed, built, and decorated. Its location is shown on the rear cover map. You are closest to the Museum at this point on the walk (see map). If you decide on a visit from here, turn left at the junction of Bartlett Street with George Street. Cross Lansdown Road and walk 150 metres along the Paragon, where it is housed in the Countess of Huntingdon's chapel on the left.

Milsom Street

Milsom Street was created in the 1760s on what were previously gardens. Built of *Bath Stone*, the buildings were originally residential. In the 1780s they had railings and gardens in front of the houses. The stones in the building on your right, on the west corner of George Street and Milsom Street, demonstrate wonderful cross bedding in the limestones, emphasised by thin, discontinuous layers and clusters of finely-ground crushed shell fragments.

Cross bedding

These sediment were deposited in shallow water where there were strong and variable currents. The cross bedding develops from the formation and movement of ripples. Sediment moves up the ripple and avalanches down the lee slope, see diagram below. Ripples provide evidence of ancient current direction. They also tell you whether or not the stone has been laid in the wall upside down. Do you think that some of these blocks are the wrong way up?

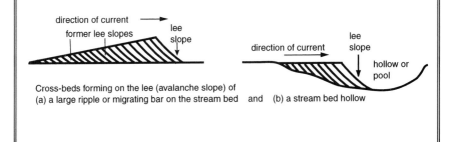

Cross-beds forming on the lee (avalanche slope) of
(a) a large ripple or migrating bar on the stream bed   and   (b) a stream bed hollow

Cladding in Milsom Street

The majority of rocks mentioned in Milsom Street are polished and used for cladding. The best examples are described below with more detail in the glossary on pages 43-44.

❏ GRANITE. The building opposite that with cross-bedding, on the other street corner, has its entrance framed in *Peterhead Granite.* You can see large salmon-pink feldspar crystals and some large darker areas. These are very good examples of 'heathens'. The lower courses of the façade in Milsom Street are large blocks of *Pennant Sandstone*. There are also *Pennant Sandstone* insets below the windows.

❏ *SERPENTINITE* can be seen on the other side of the road at No 21. This is dark green with a network of irregular veins or cracks mostly infilled with calcite.

❏ MARBLE. At No 20 (Jaeger) there is a white *Carrara marble* threshold. The marble shows zigzag folds and has suffered much deformation.

❏ GRANITE. (Gap Kids) No 17-18, is clad in *granite* with brownish feldspars and very distinctive blue-coloured quartz crystals. Blue quartz like this suggests that the igneous rock has been subjected to later deformation or strain. This *altered granite* is called Blaubrun and comes from Sweden; it dates from about 500 million years ago.

❏ LARVIKITE. Opposite at Hobbs, No 32, there is dark *larvikite* with the characteristic silvery blue iridescence of the feldspars.

❏ GRANITE. In the early 1800s the street was made into a high-class shopping area. Jolly's department store opened in 1831. In 1879 the front of the building changed again and now **Shap Granite** from Cumbria replaces the original *Bath Stone* columns and pilasters. It has beautiful, large, rectangular pink feldspars (see photo rear cover). The *Shap granite* columns are made from solid 2·5m lengths of granite. *New Red Sandstone* was used to decorate the tops of the columns and pilasters. Risers were made from a lighter variety of *Shap granite*. Green man-made material has been used at the base of the pilasters. This is probably fairly new and has replaced the sandstone.

❏ GRANITE. On the opposite side, at the Alliance and Leicester, *Shap granite* has again been used as cladding to the ground floor. There are *New Red Sandstone* arches above with crests and carved figures. The second and third storeys are built from limestone with fluted columns and Corinthian capitals.

❏ GABBRO. Fine, black *gabbro* cladding can be seen on the front of Nos 4 - 5, Waterstones. This rock is very dark so it's difficult to see the crystals.

Continue down Milsom Street and cross over the end of Quiet Street.

Look at the building on the corner of Quiet Street and Old Bond Street (Nationwide Building Society). Unpolished coarse-grained granite with large white, rectangular feldspar crystals from south-west Britain has been used for the entire ground floor with *Bath Stone* higher up. Can you see the shiny crystals of muscovite mica here? The granite masonry has pronounced banded rustication (page 7). *Gabbro* (page 43) has been used as infill panels.

Notice the variety of rocks used for kerbstones here. There is *Cornish Granite* and darker Guernsey diorite.

Now cross the road and walk down Green Street .

Note the Green Street side of Lloyds TSB. This is a good example of freestone oolite with very few shell fragments and no visible bedding.

At the bottom of Green Street turn left and walk up Broad Street some 50m, as far as The Moon and Sixpence. Turn left here into the little courtyard opposite Rossiters.

The setts beneath your feet are of *granite*.

The Moon and Sixpence Wall Game

As you enter the courtyard, pause to inspect the wall on your right. What is it made of? The wall is a very strange mixture indeed. It is typical of many old walls where appearance was not important. It used, or reused, any materials that conveniently came to hand.

It provides an opportunity to quiz yourself on how many of the stones, most of which you have seen before, you can now recognise. An appropriate section of wall to examine is illustrated in colour on the rear cover of the booklet. First find this section of wall and then, if you have a mind to play this 'wall game', see what you can identify before turning over the page where, after playing the game ourselves, we venture our own suggestions for a few of the stones.

Try looking for examples of the following:

❑ WHITE LIAS, seen at Abbey Church House (page 18).
❑ BLUE LIAS, seen in the setts in Queen Street (page 23).
❑ OOLITIC LIMESTONE, described in detail on Page 5 and well displayed at Kingsmead Square and Seven Dials (page 20).
❑ FOSSILIFEROUS LIMESTONE made from shell fragments.
❑ SANDSTONE. There are both grey and purple sandstones here.
❑ BRICKS – man-made. No prizes for getting that one but the two red bricks provide a good marker for this stretch of wall. There are also bits of wood incorporated into other parts of the wall.

The Wall at the Moon and Sixpence

A field sketch identifying some of the wide variety of stones in the wall.

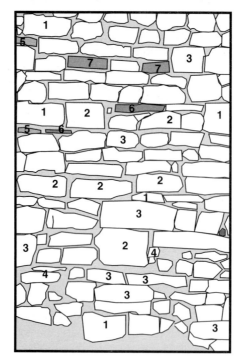

1   **WHITE LIAS**. Feel the fine soapy texture on your fingertips. This was once a very fine lime-rich mud deposited in a very shallow, low-energy sea.

2   **BLUE LIAS**. Again a fine-grained fossil-rich limestone, often rather polished. The shallow seas of the *Blue Lias* were Jurassic (page 46).

3   **OOLITIC LIMESTONE**. The ooids (page 5) should have given this one away. Again it is Jurassic.

4   **FOSSILIFEROUS LIMESTONE**. This Jurassic limestone is recognisably made up of many broken shell fragments.

5   **GREY SANDSTONE**.   **6**   **PURPLE SANDSTONE** Like all the stones above, these deposits are *sedimentary* (page 44) but compare the coarse-grained sandstone with the smooth touch of the *White Lias*. The sandstones are of Carboniferous age. How old is that? (Page 46).

7   **BRICKS**. These are very old, narrow, hand-made bricks and may have been reused many times before ending up in this wall.

When you have finished your wall examination, return to the junction between Broad Street and Green Street.

As you leave the courtyard, notice The Saracen's Head, across the road in Broad Street. This is one of the oldest pubs in Bath, virtually unaltered since it was built in 1713.

As you stand at the junction between Broad Street and Green Street, the Church opposite you is St Michael's, which originally stood just outside the old North Gate of the City. The present church is the third on this site and dates from 1837. It is built entirely of *Bath Stone*, a medium-grained oolite, showing some signs of surface crumbling in places. There are *Pennant Sandstone* steps to the main entrance and the stumps of former iron railings can also be seen.

The new building opposite is The Podium and is a modern development using *Bath Stone*.

To reach the front of the Podium, continue down Broad Street, crossing safely at the traffic lights.

Milsom and Sons, next to the Podium in Northgate Street, uses a light-coloured *larvikite* cladding on its building.

Continue south along Northgate Street, for a few metres and then make a brief diversion by descending some steep steps and walking about 6m into the alleyway.

This alleyway has an enclosed, medieval feel to it. There appears to be some of the original paving here. Flags have been used in the centre of the walkway and to each door, with the other spaces infilled with setts and a gutter down the right-hand side.

Climb back up the steps and continue along Northgate Street to the junction (left) with Bridge Street. Pause and look along the High Street, before turning down Bridge Street.

Ahead, you can see right through the tall, Gothic windows of the Abbey. It has been called 'the lantern of the west'.

The left-hand side of High Street is occupied by the imposing Guildhall (Thomas Baldwin, 1776, with a dome and wings added by John Brydon, 1891). The ground floor elevation is a good example of the impression of solidity and strength given by rustication of the stonework plus, in the central section, heavy *vermiculation* (see page 8). Above, four tall Ionic columns span the second and third storeys, which are faced with smooth ashlar. The whole façade is topped off with a massive pediment carrying the City Arms and supporting a statue of Justice (unusually, without blindfold).

Opposite the Guildhall is the entrance to 'The Corridor' with its three sets of pillars using *Peterhead Granite*. Each column is a single block of granite.

Bridge Street

Mallory's, on the corner at the top of Bridge Street, has cladding of brown *granite* with blue quartz. The threshold here uses green and white marble with *serpentinite* edgings. The next building (also Mallory's) has varieties of Swedish *granite* with red feldspars and blue quartz. A new cladding can also be seen here. This is red Ruban, a *granite* from India.

Further down Bridge Street, the next shop has sub-window cladding of **red granite** and, further down again, the shopfront of No 6 (Stitch Shop) has *Pennant Sandstone* plinths to painted columns.

The statue of Queen Victoria you can see opposite, high on the side wall of the Guildhall, is probably made from *Carrara marble*.

Continue down Bridge Street until you come to Pulteney Bridge.

Ahead, look along Argyll Street, beyond the bridge, to the fountain in Laura Place. The main bowl of the fountain was turned from a single block of *Portland Stone* and is over two metres in diameter. The original block weighed nine tonnes.

Now cross the road and turn right along Grand Parade. On the left is the River Avon. Look out over the balustrade towards the bridge.

Pulteney Bridge

This was built in 1770, again of *Bath Stone*, and is one of only three in the world to be lined with shops on both sides. The bridge was commissioned by Sir William Pulteney and designed by Robert Adam. It is the only Robert Adam building in Bath.

Look across the river at the hills opposite. The highest parts are made of the Great Oolite Limestone.

Half-way along Grand Parade, cross the road and turn right into Boat Stall Lane.

In Boat Stall Lane look left to see the old East Gate of the City built of *Bath Stone* with flags of *Pennant Sandstone* on top.

Up until the beginning of the 18th century it was possible to walk around the top of the City's fortified medieval walls. The wall with four main gates was built along the line of what was possibly the old Roman wall. Only the East Gate remains. It provided access to the river.

Continue along the lane, turn left, until you reach the square called Orange Grove.

Orange Grove

Orange Grove was so named in honour of William of Orange's visit in 1734. The obelisk here, dated 1872, has been restored and is made of *Bath Stone*.

From the edge of the central garden look back at the large building on the corner of Orange Grove and Grand Parade, with the river to its right. This was built of *Bath Stone* between 1899 and 1901 and is the most prominent Victorian landmark in Bath. Its architect was Charles Edward Davis, whose initials are woven into the ironwork over the entrance porch. The attic storeys contain architectural elements of cottage, mansion and castle.

Walk across Orange Grove to the beginning of Pierrepont Street and turn right, along Terrace Walk to York Street.

From here, look again at the hills in the distance to the south. You will see among the trees near the skyline, the turreted wall which is known as 'Sham Castle'. Ralph Allen, owner of the Combe Down Quarries and of Prior Park, ordered the building of Sham Castle to 'improve' the view from his town house and, it is said, to provide employment during one of the periodic economic downturns that affected Bath.

Cross the end of York Street and make a short diversion by turning right into the alleyway between Bridgwater House and The Huntsman pub.

This leads you to a view of Ralph Allen's remarkable town house which can be seen at the end of the alleyway over a metal gate. The elaborate Palladian façade dates from 1727, the same year as the elder Wood's first major work. The architect is unknown. As noted, when Allen lived here, he could see across to the hills where he built Sham Castle, but the house became shut in by surrounding development after he moved to Prior Park.

Return to Terrace Walk and turn right into North Parade Passage.

Twenty-five metres on the right is Sally Lunn's House. This is the only building in Bath where you can actually see the foundations (in the kitchen museum inside the shop). They reach back not just to the 12th century, when the building formed part of a large monastic estate, but as far back as the second century AD. Excavations have unearthed the remains of a Roman inn or guest house on this site.

The building you see was erected in the late 15th century; an oak beam has been dated at 1482, but it now has a 17th century façade. The gables mark it as pre-Georgian. Note the small limestone, rough-hewn building blocks and evidence of subsidence along the line of the windows.

In the close opposite, North Parade Buildings provides a fine example of classic mid-eighteenth century Georgian building.

Continue along North Parade Passage to Abbey Green.

Abbey Green

Here you can see a 200 year-old London plane tree surrounded by Stuart houses, built of *Bath Stone*. Note the 17th century public house where skeletons dating from the Middle Ages were found beneath the cellar floor. This was part of the monks' burial ground. It is possible to see the hinge of the old Abbey Gate in the wall by the archway.

On the ground floor of Abbey House and several adjacent buildings, there is a wooden lintel beam.

The carriageway contains *Pennant Sandstone* setts with some additional fossiliferous *Blue Lias.*

Look above the roof line on the north west corner to see a tall column in *Bath Stone.* This is the disguised chimney of the former Spa Laundry.

By walking north up either Church Street or Abbey Street from Abbey Green you are back in the Abbey Church Yard.

What now?

That ends the main walk covering the city centre and classical Bath. We do hope that the walk has given you as much pleasure as it gave to those who wrote it.

Did you include the 'green' loop within your main walk (see rear cover map)? If not, you may like, on this or another occasion, to use this short walk to see whether you have acquired any new skills of recognition and interpretation of the fabric of the city which surrounds you. It is a skill, of course, which can give pleasure on any urban walk you may care to make. Instructions for following the 'green' walk are shown overleaf.

The Green Southern Loop

This short additional walk starts from the junction of Stall Street with Bath Street and adds about 500m to the City Centre walk (see map on inside rear cover). It examines in more detail the use of stone on modern shop fronts. If you are unfamiliar with some of the more exotic stone used on these shop fronts, the glossary of rocks on pages 43-44 may be of help.

Shop cladding tends to change with ownership so this short walk might be more testing than planned. However, in 2001 there are good examples of the following rocks listed below.

Walk slowly down Stall Street to the south noting the range of cladding used in the buildings.

DIORITE

Diorite cladding is used on No 2 Bath Street (City Photo), in the curved arcade, on the south-west corner of Stall and Bath Streets. *Diorite* is an igneous rock which crystallised slowly from molten rock or magma. It is possible to see individual crystals. All the dark ones are silicate minerals that contain magnesium and iron, elements which impart green and black colours. The lighter ones are mostly feldspars, silicate minerals that contain calcium, sodium and potassium. Feldspars are shades of grey when pure. Yellow, pink and red tones indicate very small amounts of iron oxide impurities. There is a small amount of clear quartz which is colourless when pure and not easy to see against a dark background.

GABBRO

Further down Stall Street, on the other side of the road, black *gabbro* has been used to clad the HMV building (Nos 13-15), on the corner of Stall Street and Abbey Gate Street. *Gabbro* is an igneous rock and forms in the same way as *diorite* but it has no quartz. This *gabbro* shows a strange texture as the brownish coloured feldspar crystals form a network of interlocking elongate crystals. It is falsely called black granite in the stone trade.

MARBLE COLUMNS

On the corner between Stall Street and Abbey Gate Street is Marks and Spencer's (Nos 16-19). The cladding on the Stall Street front of Marks and Spencer's is of two types, marble in the columns and *gabbro* at the base.

GRANITE

Take a brief diversion, about 20m, down the Abbey Gate Street side of Marks and Spencer's.

Here a coarse *granite* with deep red feldspars and grey quartz is used for the large name and crest plaques mounted by the doorway. Note the polished and matt finishes. There is pale pinkish-grey *granite* cladding on the base of the walls.

Now return to Stall Street.

LARVIKITE

On the lower wall on either side of the shop (Starbuck's Café) opposite Marks and Spencer's (No 22 Stall Street) the cladding is *larvikite*. This is another igneous rock and is easy to recognise because it has a distinctive blue sheen. The lighter feldspars are interspersed with dark ferromagnesian minerals. This is the 'blue pearl', a lighter type.

Continue down Stall Street and cross Lower Borough Walls.

SERPENTINITE

There is a *serpentinite* cladding on either side of the entrance to the building on the left-hand corner (south-west corner) of Southgate and Lower Borough Walls. This is an altered igneous rock. It is patterned with veins of white calcite. There are a number of varieties and Bath contains examples from Italy and Greece.

Continue down the pedestrianised Southgate.

GRANITE

Granite is used as cladding on Mothercare (Nos 44-48), the building opposite the entrance to The Mall about half way down Southgate. The muscovite mica which is silvery and highly reflective is very noticeable here.

LARVIKITE

Further down Southgate, on the same side as Mothercare, both polished ground-level wall cladding and unpolished threshold flooring of *larvikite* can be seen on the HSBC building (No 41). Granite slabs are used on the floor inside.

TRAVERTINE

Further down still, on the right (No 40 Southgate) **travertine** is used as cladding. *Travertine* is used by McDonald's throughout the country. It is a calcareous (lime) spring deposit. The holes in this limestone are caused by bubbles of carbon dioxide, escaping at the time the rock was being deposited. The main commercial source of *travertine* today is Italy. On the right side of the entrance, a fracture zone within the *travertine* has been filled with broken material (breccia). There is a ground-level course of *diorite*.

From this location there is a clear view of the Avon river cliff and also Brunel's viaduct.

Turn sharp right from Southgate into St James Parade and walk to the junction with Corn Street.

BATH STONE

St James Parade was originally laid out in 1768 and still has Georgian buildings on either side. However, the fronts of the buildings have been converted into shops on the left-hand side while the right-hand side has been mostly restored to the original design, as domestic buildings. This street was a rare survivor of bomb damage in 1942, and subsequent redevelopment, in this part of the city.

TERRACOTTA TILES

The roofs of the buildings in St James Parade are covered with terracotta tiles and *slate*. This is also a good place to see a variety of terracotta chimney pots (see information box, page 17).

Continue along this road until you come to a triangular park on your right. Take the narrow path to the left of this park and walk about 20m along the path.

PENNANT SANDSTONE

Notice the *Pennant Sandstone* which has been used in the pillar on the building on your left. The sandstone appears to be peeling away at the surface in thin sheets. This is caused by the expansion of salt crystals in the damp outer layers of the stone, and is a weathering process called exfoliation. Notice also the beautiful carving of the *Bath Stone* at the top of the pillar.

At the other side of the park, cross the road, Lower Borough Walls, into Bilbury Lane. Continue along this lane, to the junction with Beau Street.

MORE SANDSTONE

A few metres on your right (in Beau Street) is Bellott's Hospital, rebuilt in 1859. At the base of the wall are four courses of dark, rough-hewn *Pennant Sandstone* blocks below a main wall of Jurassic limestone. *Pennant Sandstone* has also been used with the limestone as decoration over the windows (see photo).

Return to the junction with Bilbury Lane. Cross over Beau Street and continue along Bilbury Lane.

On the west corner is the new Millennium Spa Building. On the right is St Catherine's Hospital (sixteenth century, rebuilt in nineteenth century). Facing each other across this narrow lane are the old and the new in health care.

Continue along Bilbury Lane and before entering the passageway look upwards.

Above the covered passage, note the difference between old and new stonework. The new, a combination of replacement and patching, is probably made of reconstituted stone. Notice that all the pillars in the passageway stand on *Pennant Sandstone* bases.

Finally walk through the covered passage into Bath Street. This is the end of the 'Green Southern Loop'. To return to Stall Street turn right or, if you are continuing with the main walk, turn left along Bath Street towards the Cross Bath (page 15).

Glossary of Rock Names

Igneous rocks

This group of rocks has cooled and crystallised from molten rock or magma (see the Rock Cycle, page 45). If these igneous rocks cooled deep in the Earth's crust, then the crystals are large. If the magma came to the surface as lava, then it cooled quickly and the crystals are small. Some examples of igneous rocks that are found in the buildings of Bath are described below.

GRANITE is an igneous rock which cooled slowly and so the crystals are large. The crystals interlock with one another and are big enough for you to be able to see them with your naked eye in any example you look at closely. The rock is made of silicate minerals. You may recognise cream-coloured feldspars, grey quartz crystals and black biotite mica. It also sometimes contains scattered flecks of the other common mica mineral, muscovite, which is silvery and highly reflective.

DIORITE is also an igneous rock that crystallised slowly from molten rock or magma. However, it has more iron and magnesium (ferromagnesian) minerals than granite and its percentage of silica is less so although the crystal structure may look similar to granite, it is usually darker in colour.

GABBRO is another coarse, crystalline igneous rock which formed at depth but it has even less silica than *diorite* and no quartz. The main type of *gabbro* used in Bath is Rustenberg/Bon Accord from South Africa. This *gabbro* has a mottled appearance; the lighter areas are feldspars and the darker areas are ferromagnesian minerals. Another type seen in Bath is very dense and black and probably from Scandinavia.

LARVIKITE (a variety of syenite) is an igneous rock with large feldspar crystals. It is easy to recognise because it has a distinctive blue sheen from the schiller effect, or iridescence, created by light reflecting from tiny inclusions or surfaces within the feldspar crystals, which are actually composed of microscopic intergrowths of slightly different composition and refractive indices. The feldspars are interspersed with dark ferromagnesian minerals. There are two common varieties of *larvikite*, both from Norway, and you may recognise both types being used in Bath. The darker 'emerald pearl' is from high levels in the quarries whilst the lighter blue comes from low levels.

Sedimentary Rocks

Some sedimentary rocks form from materials which have been weathered and eroded from older rock, transported by rivers, the sea, wind or ice and then deposited. Over time the sediments become compacted and cemented to form rock (see the Rock Cycle, overleaf). Examples of this type of sedimentary rock that are found in the buildings of Bath are listed below.

SANDSTONE is mostly made of spherical sand (quartz) grains. The grains are rounded by long periods of transport by either water or wind and they are deposited in layers or beds. The grains are held together by 'cement' deposited by ground-water rich in either silica, calcite or iron. *Pennant Sandstone* is the most common sandstone you will see in local buildings.

BRECCIA is made of coarse angular fragments cemented together with newer, finer material. The fragments are angular because they were not transported far enough to make them rounded before they were deposited.

Some sedimentary rocks have biological and/or chemical origins. Examples of this type of sedimentary rock are listed below.

LIMESTONE Many limestones are formed from the shells and skeletons of sea creatures slowly accumulating on the sea floor and eventually becoming compacted and cemented. *Bath Stone* limestone, however, forms from tiny particles being rolled over and over in highly agitated warm sea water. Calcium carbonate precipitates in spherical layers to form ooids (page 5).

TRAVERTINE is a calcareous (lime) spring deposit, mainly from Italy. The holes in this limestone are caused by escaping bubbles of carbon dioxide and are sometimes artificially filled to give the stone greater durability.

Metamorphic rocks

These form when any rock is subjected to sufficient heat and/or pressure to alter its original characteristics (Rock Cycle, overleaf). Such changes are often associated with mountain building caused by the plates of the Earth converging.

SLATE is formed when mudstone (a sedimentary rock) is subjected to sufficient heat and pressure for minute flakes of platy minerals, such as clays and micas, to line themselves at right angles to the maximum pressure. As a consequence, slates split easily.

SLATY TUFF Tuff is a rock formed from volcanic ash. It has become slaty by being metamorphosed.

MARBLE is formed when limestone is subjected to great heat and/or pressure. If 'streaked' it probably suffered pressure as well as heat.

SERPENTINITE is an altered igneous rock and is dominated by the green mineral *Serpentine*, rich in magnesium and iron.

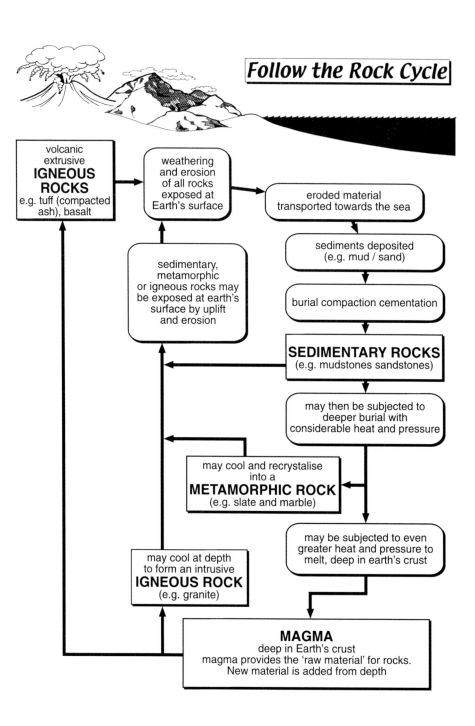

Follow the Rock Cycle

volcanic extrusive IGNEOUS ROCKS e.g. tuff (compacted ash), basalt

weathering and erosion of all rocks exposed at Earth's surface

eroded material transported towards the sea

sediments deposited (e.g. mud / sand)

sedimentary, metamorphic or igneous rocks may be exposed at earth's surface by uplift and erosion

burial compaction cementation

SEDIMENTARY ROCKS (e.g. mudstones sandstones)

may then be subjected to deeper burial with considerable heat and pressure

may cool and recrystalise into a **METAMORPHIC ROCK** (e.g. slate and marble)

may be subjected to even greater heat and pressure to melt, deep in earth's crust

may cool at depth to form an intrusive **IGNEOUS ROCK** (e.g. granite)

MAGMA deep in Earth's crust magma provides the 'raw material' for rocks. New material is added from depth

Bath in Stone, a geological time scale

Age of the beginning of each period is shown in millions of years ago. (00) indicates page numbers where reference to the stones is made. See also the Glossary of Rock Names on pages 43 and 44.

Age	Geological Period	Sedimentary	Igneous and Metamorphic
2	Quaternary	Travertine (Italy) (40)	
65	Tertiary		
146	Cretaceous		
208	Jurassic	Portland Stone, Dorset (3) (19) (25) (36) Bath Stone (5-6) etc. Blue Lias (8) (23) (33) (34) (38)	Red marble (Spain and Portugal) Carrara marble (Italy) (13) (32) (36)
247	Triassic	White Lias (8) (18) (33) (34) New Red Sandstone (30) (32)	
290	Permian		Larvikite (Norway) (30) (32) (35) (40)
363	Carboniferous	Pennant Sandstone (7) (8) etc	Granite (Cornwall) (25) (33) Dolerite (Clee Hill Dhu) (18) (26)
409	Devonian	Caithness Flags (11)	Red Granite (36) Slate (Cornwall) (17) Devonian Marble (13) Granite (Shap) (32) Granite (Peterhead) (24) (30) (32) (35)
439	Silurian		Serpentinite (Italy) (13) (32) (36) (40)
510	Ordovician		Slate (Wales) (17) Slaty tuff (Lake District) (16) (20) (21) Diorite (Guernsey) (33) (39) (40)
570	Cambrian		Slate (Wales) (17)
	Precambrian		Granite (Sweden) (32) Gabbro (S.Africa) (13) (32) (33) (39)

The oldest known rocks on earth are around 4300 million years old

Further reading, references and sources

Bezzant, N. (1980) *Out of the Rock.* Heinemann.

Buildings of Bath Museum and Bath City Council (1994)
  Stone Conservation, Advisory Booklet No 1.

Buildings of Bath Museum and Bath Preservation Trust.*The Building of Bath.*

City Centre Management's Office, B&NES Council (1997) *Bath City Trail.*

Clarke, G.(1987) *Prior Park - a Compleat Landscape.* Millstream Books.

Clifton Taylor, A. (1972) *The Pattern of English Building.* Faber & Faber.

Coysh, A.W., Mason E.J. & Waite,V. (1962. 2nd Ed) *The Mendips.* Robert Hale.

Cunliffe, B. (1986) *The City of Bath.* Alan Sutton Publishing.

de la Bédoyère, G. (1991) *The Buildings of Roman Britain.* Batsford.

Dove, J. (1995) High Street Geology in Bath. *Geology Today.* Sept-Oct,182-5.

Ison, W. (1948) *Georgian Buildings of Bath.* Faber & Faber
  (Republished by Bath Preservation Trust in 1996).

Kellaway, G.A. (1994) Environmental Factors and the Development of Bath Spa,
  Environmental Geology 24, 99-111.

Kellaway, G.A. (1996) Discovery of the Avon-Solent Fracture Zone and its
  Relationship to Bath Hot Springs, *Environmental Geology* 28 (1).

Kellaway, G.A. & Taylor, J.H. (1968):
  The Influence of Land Slipping on the Development of the City of Bath,
  xxiii Inter. Geol. Congress 12, 65-76.

McCall,J. (1999) *Gloucester in Stone.* Thematic Trails, Oxford.

Perkins, J.W., Brooks, A.T. & Pearce, A.E. McR (1990)
  Bath Stone, a Quarry History. Bath Press, Avon.

Pevensey Heritage Guide (1996) *Bath.* The Pevensey Press.

Roat, J. & Chapman, M. *Bath Historical Streetscape Survey.* Bath Arch. Trust.

Stonebridge, E. (1999) *Bristol Heritage in Stone.* Thematic Trails, Oxford.

Wooster, P. *The Stone Industry at Bath.* Bath City Archives.

This booklet has been produced by Elizabeth Devon, John Parkins and David Workman, members of the Bath Geological Society. The authors gratefully acknowledge additional material from Ruth Abbott, Martin Devon, Valerie and Victoria Griffiths and Ron Smith. Thank you also for helpful comments, additions and support from Reg Bradshaw, Peter and Janet Keene and Eric Robinson whose concept of the 'wall game' was developed at the 'Moon and Sixpence'. Photographs are by John Parkins, David Workman and Peter Keene. The cartoon on page 22 is by Allan Comer.

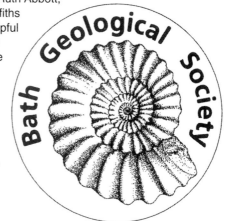

Details on the Bath Geological Society may be obtained from the secretary, Elizabeth Devon Tel. 01225 742752; email: bathgeolsoc@bath.ac.uk
Or from our web site:
http://www.bath.ac.uk/bathgeolsoc/

Cover illustrations

Front   No 20 The Circus (page 28). [photo: PK]

Rear   (top) Royal Crescent (page 26). [photo: PK]

(left) Column of *Shap Granite*, Milsom St (page 32) [photo: JP]

(right) Moon and Sixpence Wall game (page 33). [photo: DW]

(lower left) Cluster of shells, Seven Dials (page 20). [photo: PK]

Map   The rear cover map by Peter Keene is based, with permission, on a map produced for Bath Tourist Information Centre.

Thematic Trails

'Bath in Stone, a guide to the city's building stones' is published by Thematic Trails, an independent educational charity whose aim is to encourage the interpretation and appreciation of valued environments. All members of the trust give their services without charge. The trust specialises in the publication of walks which provide a stimulating, straightforward commentary, offering observations and explanation of the theme being explored and written in a form suitable for the curious visitor, educational groups, the interested non-specialist and local resident.

A selection of walks on some related topics, published by Thematic Trails are listed below. These may be obtained at information centres, museums and shops local to sites or direct from the publisher. A full catalogue is available from the publisher or from our web site: htpp://www.thematictrails.u-net.com/home.htm

Bristol, heritage in stone	Geology at Hartland Quay
Gloucester in Stone, a city walk	Strawberry Water to Marsland Mouth
Exeter in Stone, an urban geology	The Cliffs of Hartland Quay
Geology and the Buildings of Oxford	The Cliffs of Saunton
Taming the Rivers of Oxford	The Cliffs of Westward Ho!
Lyn in Flood, Watersmeet to Lynmouth	Northam Burrows Environments
Exe in Flood, an Exeter riverside walk	Braunton Burrows Ecology Trail
Dawlish Warren Ecology Trail	Valley of Rocks, Lynton
Dawlish Warren and the Sea	Westward Ho! Against the Sea

'Bath in Stone, a guide to the city's building stones' is published by Thematic Trails (editor: Peter Keene)
7 Norwood Avenue, Kingston Bagpuize, Oxfordshire OX13 5AD.
© Bath Geological Society 2001
ISBN 0 948444 38 X